Number Grids and Tiles

David Fielker and Fran Mosley

British Library Cataloguing-in-Publication Data.
A catalogue record for this book is available from the British Library.

ISBN 1 874099 50 2
Designed and typeset by Bookcraft, Stroud
Cover designed by Patrick MacAllister, London
Printed by GPS Ltd, Watford

BEAM is supported by Islington Council

Contents

Introduction

by David Fielker

Concrete and abstract

The early development of awareness about whole numbers falls very broadly into two stages, though this is a simplification that skims over the familiar intricacies of number concepts.

The first is a **concrete** stage, and is concerned with the manipulation of sets of objects which children handle, group and regroup, arrange and rearrange, and compare. In the process of all this they count objects with increasing sophistication, so that they learn number names, partly in an individual way as descriptions of the sizes of the sets of objects, and partly as a recited counting sequence.

The second stage is developed through learning how to write numerals, and is concerned with these **symbols**. The symbols are initially an alternative way of writing the number names, in the same way as written words are used to record and represent spoken words. In a way it would be easier for young children to understand numbers written as words, because this is more consistent with the general principles of written recording, where there is quite a strong correspondence between letters and sounds. The numerals are in fact more abstract than this, and although they appear on the face of it simpler than the written words, it is possible that conceptually they are more difficult, because they are a set of symbols quite separate from the alphabet, with no visual clues either to sound or to the numbers they represent.

Of course, the numerals become more complicated when we consider numbers above 9, which are represented by the same ten symbols using an intricate place value system. Children can then use this system to perform arithmetical operations like addition of two-digit numbers, but at this stage it is the symbols that are being manipulated, rather than the concrete objects. Most children quickly reach this stage of abstraction. Even a simple statement like '2 + 3 = 5' implies a generality about the three numbers concerned, regardless of what concrete objects they are describing.

One of the many advantages of number grids is that they provide a stage between the concrete and the symbolic which combines the two, as well as providing some sort of structure. This is a great help to children who are having difficulty transferring from one to the other.

The objects in this case are the squares or the tiles on which the numerals are written. The numerals imply, in a sophisticated way, that the squares need not be counted, but they are always there to be counted should the need be felt. When you write the numerals from 1 to 25 in a square, the 25 squares are there. Each time the next numeral is written, that number of squares has been filled in. If the squares are filled in in order, then the number can be checked at any stage to see that it still corresponds with the numeral. If the numerals are entered at random, this can still be done if you count only the squares that already have numerals in them.

Structure

The structure of the 25-square as a 5 by 5 array means that there are alternative ways of counting the squares: as 5 x 5; or as 5, 10, 15, 20, 25, where these numerals appear at the ends of the rows.

1	2	3	4	5
6	7	8	9	10
11	12	13	14	15
16	17	18	19	20
21	22	23	24	25

We can also see that the odd/even alternations are preserved in the columns as well as in the rows. (But not in the diagonals: why not?) We can make predictions about how this continues if the pattern is extended to higher numbers by continuing to add rows of 5. We can also compare the odd/even pattern with, say, the 6 by 6 array, where something slightly different happens.

Now the columns are alternately odd and

1	2	3	4	5	6
7	8	9	10	11	12
13	14	15	16	17	18
19	20	21	22	23	24
25	26	27	28	29	30
31	32	33	34	35	36

even. But if we focus attention on the even columns, and describe them as multiples of 2, then we can also see that the third column consists of multiples of 3. But they are the odd multiples of 3. The even multiples of 3 are in the last column, because they are also multiples of 6.

We can see that the only numbers on the grid which are not multiples of 2 or 3 must be in columns 1 or 5. This means that if we are looking for **prime** numbers (apart from those in the first row), then they must be in these two columns. Not all the numbers in these two columns are prime, as can be seen from the 25 and 35. But all primes above 3 will be found there. (A sophisticated way of explaining this, which older children will appreciate, is to say that all primes other than 2 or 3 are either one more or one less than a multiple of 6. If you like, primes are of the form $6n\pm1$.)

Now we can look back at the 5 by 5 square and ask why similar things do not happen. We do not get multiples of anything in any of the columns, apart from the last one which consists of multiples of 5.

What happens with squares of other sizes? Can we make some generalisations about when we get multiples and when we do not, and which particular sets of multiples we do get?

The 100-square provides similar opportunities, but because it is based on rows of 10, we also have some ideas about place value built into it.

Ideas about place value can be reinforced by considering what happens on the 100-square if you move one square to the right, or one square down. We can extend this 'spatial' arithmetic to considering movement of several squares to the right or down, and combinations of the two. What happens if you move to the left, or up? These movements help to explain some of the number patterns discussed later. For example, combining one down with one to the left is equivalent to adding 10 and subtracting 1 (or

adding 9); this explains the diagonal lines produced by colouring in the multiples of 9. Other patterns can be explained in similar ways.

Work with younger children

Place value does not necessarily come automatically, as the following anecdote shows.

Jason was six years old. He was putting number tiles onto a 100-square. There seemed to be about three sets of tiles.

He picked up 31, but held it upside down. He held it near the 13 which was printed on the 100-square, and pondered for a while. Then he put it back in the box.

He picked up 36.

"Can you read it?" I asked.

"Three and then six," he said.

He found the third row, then moved along to the sixth column, and put the tile on top of the 36 on the 100-square.

Jason placed other tiles in the same way. It is easy to identify his failures, and his lack of understanding. But if one is to build on success and understanding, it is better to concentrate on what Jason was able to do. In spite of his poor reading of the numerals and his occasional difficulties over their orientation, he had a perfectly good system for placing the tiles in their correct places. 'Three and then six' was interpreted as a sort of coordinate system, in which each two-digit numeral was read as a pair of coordinates, the first indicating the row and the second indicating the column[1]. This is very similar to the conventional system of coordinate geometry, where, say, (3,6) is interpreted as a point which is reached by starting at the origin on the graph and moving 3 to the right and 6 up.

Jason's origin was the top left hand square, and in effect he moved down and then across. One could say he understood coordinate geometry! Whether or not he also understood place value is a different matter, but he certainly

---

[1] There is a slight complication here in that the numbering of the rows begins with 0, and the numbering of the columns begins with 1, but Jason seemed to have sorted this out.

understood one of its components, the idea that the two digits of a numeral mean different things.

It is probably a good idea for younger children to carry out the exercise that Jason was attempting, and fill in a hundred square in this way. They can do it with tiles on a printed diagram, and they can do it, probably later, by putting tiles on an empty square.

We used to have available a hundred board, which had an array of 10 by 10 hooks, on which children could hang discs with the numbers from 1 to 100 printed on them. They usually began by looking among the pile of discs for 1, then for 2, and so on. They soon realised the inefficiency of this method, and instead picked up whatever came first to hand, and worked out where it should go. Sometimes they counted from the beginning in ones, but eventually they thought in the same sort of way that Jason did: 36 would be put in the fourth row because it was 30-something and that was where the 30s went, and then in the sixth column because it was 36.

Thus they improved upon their place value skills, using the concrete nature of the hundred board which made counting of squares — or of rows and columns — possible, but they were still using the abstract ideas of the place value system based on the numerals.

The 'hidden numbers' activities suggested on various pages of this book are an example of ways to help children become thoroughly familiar with the structure.

Pattern is an important idea in mathematics. By pattern we mean some sort of regularity, and this is something about which young children need to learn. (A typical story is of the five-year-old girl who threaded beads coloured red, yellow, red, yellow, red, yellow. She then put in a green one, and when asked why, said, "Because green is my favourite colour!")

The colouring-in of 'tables' patterns on the 1–100 square is a useful activity just to encourage the idea of regularity. Even if the multiplication tables are not known, some of the ideas are embodied in, say, colouring in every third number from 3, or if one prefers, missing two, colouring, missing two, colouring, and so on.

1 2 _3_ 4 5 _6_ 7 8 _9_ 10

11 _12_ 13 14 _15_ 16 17 _18_ 19 20

_21_ 22 . . .

Some children will notice the 'diagonal' stripes appearing and use this as a check on their accuracy, or perhaps after a while continue the stripes because it is quicker! The teacher will note those who, after an error, experience a discontinuity in the colour pattern but do not notice it.

The **tiles**, as indicated above, can be used by younger children in conjunction with the 100-square or with squares of other sizes. They can be used for putting numerals in order, going upwards or going downwards. And they can be used for sorting.

Sorting is probably best done, at least initially, by letting children choose their own attributes. Here they will perhaps choose odd or even numbers, or numbers above or below a particular number, or numbers which contain a certain digit. The freedom to make their own choice reinforces the idea of a criterion for choice, the selection of a rule for the set of numbers being sorted. Like the idea of pattern, this is not always an idea that comes naturally without some work on it. Obviously they will also meet such ideas in other sorting activities, but the tiles give an opportunity to sort numbers, rather than logiblocks or other more concrete materials. The point is that children at this stage will not necessarily choose attributes that are numerical: one girl sorted the following from the numbers up to 20:

2, 3, 10, 12, 13, 20

Even her teacher was baffled, until she remembered she had been doing some work on phonics!

Analogues and arrays

The number line is also an example of a number grid, but in one dimension instead of two. However, there is another important difference which is a feature of the modern number line.

Old number lines used indeed to be one-dimensional number grids, rather like a row of number tiles.

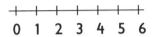

They gave rise to some difficulties, typified by games like Ludo, where children had to count on from where they were. A young child with a counter on, say, 2, who then threw a 3, would count "One, two, three," starting with the square they were already on, and land on 4 instead of 5. In the more formal setting of the number line this would transfer into '2 + 3 = 4'!

This difficulty was one factor in deciding that number lines should be based on length as an analogue for the whole numbers, rather than squares.

$$+ \quad + \quad + \quad + \quad + \quad + \quad +$$
$$0 \quad 1 \quad 2 \quad 3 \quad 4 \quad 5 \quad 6$$

Notice that now the line starts with 0 rather than 1, and a child finding the result of 2 + 3 could start from 0 and count on first two and then three, or start from the 2 and just count on three. The previous error was avoided.

It is a matter of philosophy, perhaps, as to whether you should avoid the error in this way. Avoiding an error often means that the misconceptions which create the error are never faced, and perhaps not examined and corrected. Maybe we need both types of number line, in order to face up to any misconceptions, and to encourage flexibility of thought in children. And they will still play games like Ludo!

Certainly one advantage of the length analogue number line is that we can also deal with fractions. The number line based on squares definitely supports only ideas about whole numbers.

This is also true about two-dimensional number grids: they are concerned with whole numbers only. Therefore the ideas which can be developed are those to do with whole numbers.

This still gives us plenty of opportunity to concern ourselves with mathematical ideas such as: notation and place value; the operations of addition, subtraction, multiplication and division; properties of numbers; squares and square roots; multiples and divisors; prime numbers; and large numbers. There is also scope for recognising patterns and relationships, making generalisations, and giving explanations.

Patterns and problems

The two-dimensional feature of number grids in general raises possibilities for exploring number patterns in a richer way. We can work on either rows or columns, or on both simultaneously. We can look at diagonals, like those on the 100-square for the pattern of threes or nines or elevens. We can look at other patterns that cut across rows and columns, like those made by the multiples of 4, 6, or 7. We can contrast the dullness of the patterns of twos or fives or tens, and explain why they are dull here, but not on the 9x9 square where they become more interesting, and we can generalise this to other sizes of square.

One important idea is that whatever pattern is started, it can continue indefinitely, just like the numbers themselves. This gives scope for ideas about exactly how it will continue, with various levels of sophistication, according to the children, about explanation, justification and proof.

For instance, colouring in the **square** numbers on a 100-square produces some sort of regularity:

1	2	3	4	5	6	7	8	9	10
11	12	13	14	15	16	17	18	19	20
21	22	23	24	25	26	27	28	29	30
31	32	33	34	35	36	37	38	39	40
41	42	43	44	45	46	47	48	49	50
51	52	53	54	55	56	57	58	59	60
61	62	63	64	65	66	67	68	69	70
71	72	73	74	75	76	77	78	79	80
81	82	83	84	85	86	87	88	89	90
91	92	93	94	95	96	97	98	99	100

Although the spacing between the rows is somewhat irregular (why?), the squares appear in columns 1, 4, 9, 6, 5, 6, 9, 4, 1, 0; and then repeat this sequence. Why is this? And why is the sequence palindromic? The squares never appear in columns 2, 3, 7 or 8. Why is this?[2] Will these rules continue? What is the next square number

---

[2] Look at what happens to the digits.

to appear in column 1? (See p.9 for some explanations.)

Similar ideas can be explored with respect to the pattern for **triangular** numbers:

1
3 = 1 + 2
6 = 1 + 2 + 3
10 = 1 + 2 + 3 + 4
and so on

What happens with **cubes**?

An exploration of **prime** numbers can be conducted in similar ways, but one method of producing the primes on the hundred square is to eliminate the non-primes. 1 is not a prime[3], so that can go first. Then we shade out the multiples of 2, except 2 itself; then the multiples of 3 above 3; and so on. It will become evident, if it is not so in advance, that it is not necessary to eliminate the multiples of 4, since these have already disappeared in the elimination of multiples of 2, and already some simple relationships between multiples are established. The children will also need to discuss how far it is necessary to go with this elimination.[4]

What remains are the primes. These have no pattern, as will be seen. However, children will need to make some explorations in order to find this out. (The only certainty is that, apart from 2, all the primes are odd, but this needs some discussion.)

The children may consider how many primes there are in successive rows. The first two rows each contain four primes, but this does not happen again up to 100. Successive rows then contain two or three primes, until the last row, which only contains only one. If the rows are continued past 100, there are questions we can ask. Will there be another row with four primes? Which next row contains only one? Will there be a row with no primes? Will there be two successive

rows, or more, without primes?

As well as these overall patterns, there are also 'local' patterns which are also generally true. Consider a square of four squares anywhere on the 100-square.

46 47
56 57

What do you notice about the four numbers? One thing is that if you add the numbers in pairs diagonally, 46 + 57 = 56 + 47.

Now take any rectangle, and do the same thing with the numbers in the corners. Why does the same result occur? In fact, the square or rectangle does not need to have sides horizontal and vertical. Indeed, this will also work for any parallelogram. So this is also an interesting geometrical exercise.

The small square above has another interesting property: 46 x 57 = 2622, and 47 x 56 = 2632. Try with different squares of four: the products always differ by 10. Why is this? What happens with the numbers at the corners of larger squares, or of rectangles?

Other arrays

There are other ways of writing numbers in the squares. Start in a corner:

1   2   4   7 . . .
3   5   8 . . .
6   9 . . .
10 . . .

Look at where the triangular numbers lie. Explore sequences of numbers in rows or columns, or along diagonals. Colour in different sets of multiples.

Start in the centre and write the numbers in a spiral:

21 . . .

20 7   8   9 10
19 6   1   2 11
18 5   4   3 12
17 16 15 14 13

---

[3] There is a theorem that any number can be expressed uniquely as a product of prime factors. If 1 were prime, then we could for instance express 6 as 2 x 3, 1 x 2 x 3, 1 x 1 x 2 x 3, and so on, inserting 1 as many times as we liked, and the theorem would break down.

[4] When the multiples of 7 have been removed that is in fact sufficient, because the multiples of 11 (the next prime) have already been removed up to 99.

Colour in sets of multiples. Note the square numbers. Note the primes (a large number of primes appear to lie on diagonals). Find rules for sequences of numbers in rows or columns, extend them, and check the results.

Try a different triangular arrangement:

$$1$$
$$2 \quad 3 \quad 4$$
$$5 \quad 6 \quad 7 \quad 8 \quad 9$$
. . .

Where have the triangular numbers gone? What are the numbers at the ends of the rows? Why?

Children will also think of their own arrays, like the 'snakes and ladders' array:

1	2	3	4	5	6	7	8	9	10
20	19	18	17	16	15	14	13	12	11
21	22	. . .							

This has some properties similar to those of the ordinary 100-square.

Properties and relationships

Many of the later activities involve ideas about numbers and relationships between them.

The idea of multiples of any number becomes more complicated when one considers relationships between different sets of multiples, as in *Patterns of multiples* on p.13 and *Multiple patterns* on p.53. Multiples of 6 are also multiples of 3. Numbers which are multiples of both 4 and 5 are multiples of 20. Numbers which are multiples of both 4 and 6 are multiples of 12[5].

Some of the 100-square activities focus attention on **last digits**, the most explicit of which is *Columns* on p.14. But, for instance, the colouring-in of square numbers indicates that these only come in certain columns, and squares therefore never end in 2, 3, 7 or 8. To explain this one needs to square each digit in turn.

$0^2 = 0$, $1^2 = 1$, $2^2 = 4$, $3^2 = 9$, $4^2 = 16$, $5^2 = 25$, $6^2 = 36$, $7^2 = 49$, $8^2 = 64$, $9^2 = 81$

It is a fairly sophisticated idea, but since when squaring higher numbers the tens digits and above cannot affect the units digits, the palindromic[6] sequence of last digits will continue. Similar considerations will explain why other sets of numbers only appear in certain columns.

Some of the **sequences** that are discussed in conjunction with the 1–100 square spiral are difficult to find a definite rule for. However, it is enough that children work on the idea of successive differences.

The first sequence dealt with is:

2, 11, 28, 53, 86, . . .

It is difficult to see any sort of relationship immediately. However, successive differences are:

9, 17, 26, 33, . . .

and if we look at the differences of these then they are:

8, 8, 8, . . .

A rule becomes clear, which can now be referred back to the first row of numbers: for instance, the next difference after 33 will be 8 more — that is 41 — so the next number in the original sequence will be 86 + 41 = 127. We can thus predict the next few numbers, and continue the spiral in order to verify them. We need not do much more at this stage[7]. Indeed, it is an important aspect of mathematics that if we can predict what higher numbers are going to continue in the sequence then we do not actually have to extend the spiral.

---

[5] An old-fashioned term for this idea was 'lowest common multiple', a one-time essential for adding fractions.

[6] As with sequences of letters, a palindromic sequence of numbers is one that reads the same forwards as backwards.

[7] The sequence is a quadratic one, but there is time enough for that when the children are older.

Problems and puzzles

The tiles in particular lend themselves to those sorts of puzzles in which numbers have to be put in positions according to certain rules. Using the tiles enables us to move the numbers around easily.

An initial strategy for solution will usually be trial and error but, as solutions appear, some patterns may emerge that will warrant some explanation.

A simple example is the first 'zigzag' on p.75, in which the numbers 1 to 9 are to be inserted so that the total of each arm is the same.

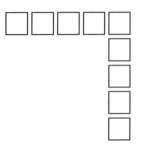

Trial and error will quickly lead to a solution, but not without some mental calculation. We can then ask the children what different numbers can be put in the corner square, and it will become apparent that they always have to be odd. Why is this? Well, since the two arms are to be equal, the total overall without the corner square must be even. Since the sum of the numbers from 1 to 9 is odd (one can actually do the addition, or merely note that there are five odd numbers), the number in the corner must be odd.

Such logical argument, based on properties of numbers, is also possible in the rest of the puzzles. However, in some cases the argument is much more complicated, and may be possible only for older and/or brighter children. This does not mean that others cannot continue to blend trial and error with an increasing amount of number awareness as patterns emerge. Children always surprise us with their insights, and these puzzles give opportunity for them.

Photocopiable sheets and activities

Number grid jigsaws

Jigsaws

Cut up the number grid along the lines. Can you fit
the pieces back together again?
Can your friend fit the pieces back together again?
(If it's too hard, try placing the pieces on a number
grid that hasn't been cut up.)

Hide one or two of the pieces and challenge your
friend to do the jigsaw. Can she say what numbers are
missing?

Jumble up the pieces from two jigsaws. Can you sort
them and do the two jigsaws?

Use some squared paper to make a number jigsaw of
your own. It doesn't have to be square — it could be
a rectangle, or even a cross!

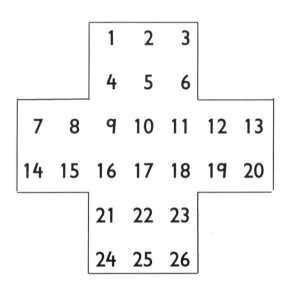

Grid 1 (top-left):

1	2	3	4
5	6	7	8
9	10	11	12
13	14	15	16

Grid 2 (top-right):

0	1	2	3
4	5	6	7
8	9	10	11
12	13	14	15

Grid 3 (middle-left):

1	2	3	4	5
6	7	8	9	10
11	12	13	14	15
16	17	18	19	20
21	22	23	24	25

Grid 4 (middle-right):

0	1	2	3	4
5	6	7	8	9
10	11	12	13	14
15	16	17	18	19
20	21	22	23	24

Grid 5 (bottom-left):

1	2	3	4	5	6
7	8	9	10	11	12
13	14	15	16	17	18
19	20	21	22	23	24
25	26	27	28	29	30
31	32	33	34	35	36

Grid 6 (bottom-right):

0	1	2	3	4	5
6	7	8	9	10	11
12	13	14	15	16	17
18	19	20	21	22	23
24	25	26	27	28	29
30	31	32	33	34	35

1	2	3	4	5	6	7
8	9	10	11	12	13	14
15	16	17	18	19	20	21
22	23	24	25	26	27	28
29	30	31	32	33	34	35
36	37	38	39	40	41	42
43	44	45	46	47	48	49

0	1	2	3	4	5	6
7	8	9	10	11	12	13
14	15	16	17	18	19	20
21	22	23	24	25	26	27
28	29	30	31	32	33	34
35	36	37	38	39	40	41
42	43	44	45	46	47	48

Number grid jigsaw

1	2	3	4	5	6	7	8	9	10
11	12	13	14	15	16	17	18	19	20
21	22	23	24	25	26	27	28	29	30
31	32	33	34	35	36	37	38	39	40
41	42	43	44	45	46	47	48	49	50
51	52	53	54	55	56	57	58	59	60
61	62	63	64	65	66	67	68	69	70
71	72	73	74	75	76	77	78	79	80
81	82	83	84	85	86	87	88	89	90
91	92	93	94	95	96	97	98	99	100

Incomplete number grids

Missing numbers

Can you fill in the missing numbers?

When you have filled in the missing numbers, place a cube on any number on the grid. Can your friend tell you what number is hidden?
Can they write the number down?

Make an incomplete number grid of your own for a friend to complete.

Grid 1

0			3
4		6	7
8		10	
12			15

Grid 2

1		3	4
5			8
			12
	14		

Grid 3

0	1		3	
5	6		8	9
	11	12		
	16		18	
20	21			24

Grid 4

1			4	5
	7		9	10
11		13		
16		18		20
	22			25

Grid 5

0			3	4	
6	7			10	
12		14		16	17
	19		21		23
		26		28	
30	31			34	35

Grid 6

1	2			5	6
7			10		12
		15		17	
	20		22		
25		27		29	30
31		33		35	36

Incomplete 1-100 grid

1	2	3		5		7		9	10
11	12			15	16		18	19	20
		23	24		26		28		30
31		33	34			37	38	39	
41	42				46			49	
51		53		55			58		60
	62	63	64			67	68		70
71	72			75		77			
	82	83		85		87			
		93	94	95		97		99	

0	1		3	4			7	8	9
10	11		13	14	15	16	17		19
20			23	24		26	27	28	29
30	31	32	33		35		37		
	41		43	44	45	46			49
	51				55			58	59
60	61		63	64	65	66	67	68	
70	71						77	78	
	81	82			85	86			
			93	94			97	98	99

1–100 square grids

Jigsaws

Cut up one of the grids into five pieces (or three, or seven . . .). Can you fit the pieces back together again? Can your friend fit the pieces back together again? (If it's too hard, try placing the pieces on a 1–100 grid that hasn't been cut up.)

Hidden numbers

Place a Centicube on any number on the grid. Can your friend tell you what number is hidden? Can they write that number down?

Place a Centicube on every number on the 1–100 grid. Can you uncover any number your friend asks for? Leave the cube off if you get it right.

I'm thinking of a number but I shan't tell you what it is. You must guess it by asking questions. I shall only answer 'yes' or 'no'. What is the fewest questions you need to ask and still guarantee you will always get my number?

Choose a number between 1 and 100 and write it down. Think up some clues about that number. Use a 1–100 grid to help you think of the clues. Try to make sure that the clues, when taken together, can apply only to your number. Can your friends work out what number it is?

Opposite corners

Draw a 2 x 2 square anywhere on a 1–100 grid. What do you notice about the numbers in the square? If you add pairs of opposite corners together (for example, 34 and 45, 35 and 44) what do you notice? Try this with other 2 x 2 squares on the same 1–100 grid. What happens on different grids (for instance, a 1–25 grid)?

Find the numbers 26, 34, 47 and 55. Are they at the corners of a square? Add the numbers at the opposite corners of this square and see what happens. Can you explain this?

Find other squares like this and see what happens with them. What happens on different grids (for instance, a 1–25 grid)? What happens with other sized squares? Or rectangles? Or parallelograms?

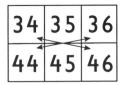 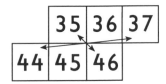

Try all the above ideas but *multiply* opposite corners together. What happens now? Why does it happen? *(see the Introduction, p.8)*

Moves

Start on any number. What number comes to the right of it? Repeat this with other numbers. What happens each time? What happens with numbers in the right-hand column? What happens if you move two to the right? One to the left?

Start on any number. What number comes below it? Repeat this with other numbers. What happens each time? What happens with numbers on the bottom row? What happens if you move two down each time?

Start on any number. Move one to the right and one down. What number are you on? Repeat this with other numbers. What happens each time? Can you explain this?

Make up other moves, try them out, and explain them. (You could use the oblong grid on page 50.)

Patterns of multiples
(see the Introduction, p.9)

Colour in 3 and the other multiples of 3. What pattern do you notice? Why does it happen? Write down those numbers and see if you can find any further patterns.

Colour in 5 and the other multiples of 5. Why do the coloured numbers only come in two columns? What other multiples give you a pattern of columns?

Colour in the 9 times table. Explain the pattern. Why is there at least one coloured number in each row? Are there any blank columns? Why not? Which row has two coloured numbers coloured? Why? Is it possible to have three numbers coloured in a row? Why not? Compare the pattern of the 3s with the pattern of the 9s.

Colour in 4 and the other multiples of 4. Why are there some columns with no squares coloured? What happens in each column where there are coloured squares? Why do the rows have alternately two and three numbers coloured in? What has this number pattern got in common with a knight's move in chess? Why?

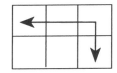

Colour in the multiples of 8. Compare the pattern with that for the 4s. Which columns are left blank? Why is that?

Colour in the multiples of 6. Compare the pattern with that for the 3s. Which columns are left blank? Why is that?

Compare the pattern of the multiples of 9 with the pattern of the 6s.

Before you colour in the multiples of 7 decide whether you think every column will have numbered squares in it. Now try it and see.

Colour in the multiples of 11. Why is the pattern that way?

Colour in multiples of 12, 13, . . . Explain what you get each time.

Which multiples give diagonal lines? Why do they?

Which multiples give knight's moves? Why do they?

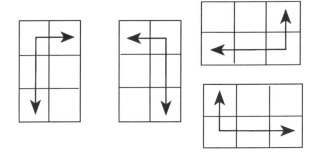

Shade all the even numbers with a light pencil. What patterns do you notice? Now put stripes on all the multiples of 3. Which numbers are shaded *and* striped? Why is that? Which numbers have no shades *or* stripes? What does that mean?

What would you expect to happen if you did the same thing for multiples of 4 and multiples of 6? Why? Try it. Were you right? What will happen with multiples of 3 and multiples of 6? Repeat this with other pairs.

What happens if you do it with multiples of 3, or multiples of 4 or multiples of 5?

Choose a multiple and explore it on the 1–100 square and on other squares (9 x 9, 8 x 8, 12 x 12 and so on). What are all the patterns it makes? Are any patterns the same? Why is that?

Other patterns
(see the Introduction, pp.6-8)

Colour in the first square then every third square (i.e. 1, 4, 7, 10 . . .). What patterns do you notice this time? Why does it happen? Try the same thing with every fifth (or tenth/ seventh/fourth) square.

Colour in the multiples of 9 and write down the numbers you have coloured. Take each coloured number in turn and add its digits together. What happens? Why does this happen? What happens with numbers past 90? Past 100? (When you add the digits of 99 you get 18. You could add *those* digits too, to get 9.)

What happens when you try colouring in multiples of 5 and adding the digits of those numbers? What patterns do you make?

Colour in all the square numbers. What do you notice? Which columns do they come in? Which are left blank? Why is that?
Why are there no square numbers in certain columns? If the 1–100 square grid were continued downwards past 100 would those columns still be blank? What would happen?

The triangular numbers are 1, 3, 6, 10 and so on.

$$1 = 1$$
$$3 = 1 + 2$$
$$6 = 1 + 2 + 3$$
$$10 = 1 + 2 + 3 + 4$$

and so on.

Colour in all the triangular numbers. What do you notice? Which columns do they come in? Which are left blank? Why is that?
If the 1–100 square grid were continued downwards past 100 would those columns still be blank? What would happen?

The cube numbers are 1, 8, 27, 64 and so on.

$$1 = 1 \times 1 \times 1$$
$$8 = 2 \times 2 \times 2$$
$$27 = 3 \times 3 \times 3$$
$$64 = 4 \times 4 \times 4$$

and so on.

Colour in all the cube numbers. What do you notice? Which columns do they come in? Which are left blank? Why is that?
If the 1–100 square grid were continued downwards past 100 would those columns still be blank? What would happen?

Make up some other special numbers (like cubes and triangular numbers). Colour them in and see what happens.

Primes
(see the Introduction, p.8)

Colour 1. Colour all the multiples of 2 except 2.
Colour all the multiples of 3 except 3 . . . and so on.
Do you now need to colour all the multiples of 4 except 4? Why not?
Colour all the multiples of 5 except 5.

What do you need to do about multiples of 6? Can you explain this?
What about multiples of 8, 9, 10, 11, . . ?
Which numbers are left? These are the prime numbers 2, 3, 5, 7, 11 and so on. What can you say about them?

Mark all the prime numbers on a 1–100 square grid. Which columns have no primes in? Why is that?
What is the next prime after 100?
How many primes are there in each row? In each column? Can you see a pattern?
The first two rows are the only ones with four primes in. If the 100 grid were continued do you think there would be another row with four primes in? Find out.
Will there be a row with no primes at all?
Make up some other questions about primes.

Explore the same problems on other grids.
In particular, look at the numbers 1 to 100 arranged in rows of 6 (see the grid on p.51). Why do the primes mostly come in the first and fifth columns? Which columns have no prime? Why is that?
If you were trying to find the primes between 100 and 200 which numbers would you test? Try it with the help of a calculator. (You could use the oblong grid on p.52.)

Overlays

Mark the multiples of 6 on an overlay, then put it back the wrong way round. What numbers are marked now? What pattern is there? Why?
Try placing the overlay in all possible positions.
Try this with other numbers.

Columns

Add a number in the first column to a number in the second column. Which column is your answer in? Try with other numbers from the first and second columns. What happens? Why is that?
Add a number in the second column to a number in the third column. Which column is your answer in? Try with other numbers from those columns. What happens? Why is that?

Try this with different columns.

What happens if you double any number in a column? What column is the answer in? Is it always the same?

What happens if you multiply numbers from two columns?
What column is the answer in? Is it always the same?

What happens if you square a number in a column?

Start with 1 and double it. Which column is the answer in? Keep on doubling and make a list of the columns in which the answers appear.
Can you explain this?

Experiment with trebling or some other idea . . .

Games

Up the squares and down the primes
Put your counters on 1. Toss a dice and move that many steps along the number track. If you land on a square number, move to the next square number.
If you land on a prime number, move back to the previous prime number.
At the end, you must wait until you throw the right number to land on 100.

Vary the rules. Or invent another game based on this, such as *Up the threes and down the fives*. Does your game work well? If not, why not?

Devise a number quiz where the answers form a pattern on a number square. Do the quiz with your group. Does everyone get the pattern?

Other ideas

Start with a square of numbers (for example, 3, 4, 13 and 14). Add all four together.
Now move a place to the right and add the new numbers together.
What happens to the total?
If you move another place to the right, what do you expect to happen this time?
Try it and see.

3 4
13 14

4 5
14 15

Start with a triangle of numbers such as 2, 3 and 12. Add all three together.
Now move a place to the right and add the new numbers together.
What happens to the total?

If you move another place to the right, what do you expect to happen this time?
Try it and see.
Choose any 2-digit number to be your starting number and write it down. Reverse the number and write that down too.
Find the difference between the two numbers and colour that number on the square.
Do this about ten times with different starting numbers.
What do you notice about the coloured squares?
What do you think is happening? Why?

You need two 1–100 grids. Pick two consecutive numbers from one grid, add them (on a calculator if you want), and colour in the total on the other grid.
Which numbers are getting coloured in?
Which numbers don't get coloured in?
Why does this happen?
Pick any number and challenge a friend to make it by adding two consecutive numbers. Can she do it?
Now do the same with three consecutive numbers, four consecutive numbers, . . .

Make an L-shape from card and place it over the 1, 11 and 12 on the 100-square. Add together the numbers that are covered and write down the total.

	2	3	4	5	6
		13	14	15	16
21	22	23	24	25	26
31	32	33	14	35	36
41	42	43	44	45	46

Now move the L-shape sideways one square, add the hidden numbers, and write down the total.
What has happened? Why?
Guess what will happen when you move the L-shape along again, then try it and see.
What happens if you move down instead of across?
What happens if you make an L-shape to cover four squares?

Try this with other shapes.

1–100 grid (left to right)

1	2	3	4	5	6	7	8	9	10
11	12	13	14	15	16	17	18	19	20
21	22	23	24	25	26	27	28	29	30
31	32	33	34	35	36	37	38	39	40
41	42	43	44	45	46	47	48	49	50
51	52	53	54	55	56	57	58	59	60
61	62	63	64	65	66	67	68	69	70
71	72	73	74	75	76	77	78	79	80
81	82	83	84	85	86	87	88	89	90
91	92	93	94	95	96	97	98	99	100

1–100 grid (right to left)

10	9	8	7	6	5	4	3	2	1
20	19	18	17	16	15	14	13	12	11
30	29	28	27	26	25	24	23	22	21
40	39	38	37	36	35	34	33	32	31
50	49	48	47	46	45	44	43	42	41
60	59	58	57	56	55	54	53	52	51
70	69	68	67	66	65	64	63	62	61
80	79	78	77	76	75	74	73	72	71
90	89	88	87	86	85	84	83	82	81
100	99	98	97	96	95	94	93	92	91

1–100 grid (bottom left to top right)

91	92	93	94	95	96	97	98	99	100
81	82	83	84	85	86	87	88	89	90
71	72	73	74	75	76	77	78	79	80
61	62	63	64	65	66	67	68	69	70
51	52	53	54	55	56	57	58	59	60
41	42	43	44	45	46	47	48	49	50
31	32	33	34	35	36	37	38	39	40
21	22	23	24	25	26	27	28	29	30
11	12	13	14	15	16	17	18	19	20
1	2	3	4	5	6	7	8	9	10

Grid 1

1	2	3	4	5	6	7	8	9	10
11	12	13	14	15	16	17	18	19	20
21	22	23	24	25	26	27	28	29	30
31	32	33	34	35	36	37	38	39	40
41	42	43	44	45	46	47	48	49	50
51	52	53	54	55	56	57	58	59	60
61	62	63	64	65	66	67	68	69	70
71	72	73	74	75	76	77	78	79	80
81	82	83	84	85	86	87	88	89	90
91	92	93	94	95	96	97	98	99	100

Grid 2

1	2	3	4	5	6	7	8	9	10
11	12	13	14	15	16	17	18	19	20
21	22	23	24	25	26	27	28	29	30
31	32	33	34	35	36	37	38	39	40
41	42	43	44	45	46	47	48	49	50
51	52	53	54	55	56	57	58	59	60
61	62	63	64	65	66	67	68	69	70
71	72	73	74	75	76	77	78	79	80
81	82	83	84	85	86	87	88	89	90
91	92	93	94	95	96	97	98	99	100

Grid 3

1	2	3	4	5	6	7	8	9	10
11	12	13	14	15	16	17	18	19	20
21	22	23	24	25	26	27	28	29	30
31	32	33	34	35	36	37	38	39	40
41	42	43	44	45	46	47	48	49	50
51	52	53	54	55	56	57	58	59	60
61	62	63	64	65	66	67	68	69	70
71	72	73	74	75	76	77	78	79	80
81	82	83	84	85	86	87	88	89	90
91	92	93	94	95	96	97	98	99	100

Grid 4

1	2	3	4	5	6	7	8	9	10
11	12	13	14	15	16	17	18	19	20
21	22	23	24	25	26	27	28	29	30
31	32	33	34	35	36	37	38	39	40
41	42	43	44	45	46	47	48	49	50
51	52	53	54	55	56	57	58	59	60
61	62	63	64	65	66	67	68	69	70
71	72	73	74	75	76	77	78	79	80
81	82	83	84	85	86	87	88	89	90
91	92	93	94	95	96	97	98	99	100

Grid 5

1	2	3	4	5	6	7	8	9	10
11	12	13	14	15	16	17	18	19	20
21	22	23	24	25	26	27	28	29	30
31	32	33	34	35	36	37	38	39	40
41	42	43	44	45	46	47	48	49	50
51	52	53	54	55	56	57	58	59	60
61	62	63	64	65	66	67	68	69	70
71	72	73	74	75	76	77	78	79	80
81	82	83	84	85	86	87	88	89	90
91	92	93	94	95	96	97	98	99	100

Grid 6

1	2	3	4	5	6	7	8	9	10
11	12	13	14	15	16	17	18	19	20
21	22	23	24	25	26	27	28	29	30
31	32	33	34	35	36	37	38	39	40
41	42	43	44	45	46	47	48	49	50
51	52	53	54	55	56	57	58	59	60
61	62	63	64	65	66	67	68	69	70
71	72	73	74	75	76	77	78	79	80
81	82	83	84	85	86	87	88	89	90
91	92	93	94	95	96	97	98	99	100

Blank 10 x 10 grids

Making your own number grids

Can you fill in the numbers from 1 to 100 in order on this blank grid?
Place a cube on any number on your grid. Can your friend tell you what number is hidden?
Can they write that number down?

Make number tiles from a numbered 1–100 grid, stuck onto card and cut into a hundred squares.
Can you place these number tiles in the correct order on the blank grid?
Now take the tiles off again. Pick one at random. Can you find where it belongs on the blank grid?
Look at a numbered grid to check whether you were right.
(Both the 1–100 grid and the blank grid could be enlarged on the photocopier.)

Can you fill in the numbers from 1 to 100 arranged in a spiral? Is your spiral the same as your friend's?
How are they the same/different?
Place a cube on every number on your grid. Can you uncover any number your friend asks for?
Leave the cube off if you get it right.

Find other ways of arranging the numbers from 1 to 100 in order on the grid.

Can you fill in the numbers from 0 to 99 in order?

Can you fill in the numbers from 100 to 199 in order?
Place a cube on any number on your grid. Can your friend tell you what number is hidden?
Can they write that number down?

Write '0' on the top left square of the grid. You are going to construct a 0–99 grid, and here is how to do it. Spin two 0–9 spinners and use the numbers you get to make a two-digit number. Write that number in the correct place on the grid. Go on doing this until you have finished.
Did you get all the numbers in the correct place?

Multiplication grids and others

(See p.58 for more on multiplication grids)

Stick a blank 10 x 10 grid onto paper. Make a multiplication grid for the numbers up to 10 x 10. Where are the square numbers on your grid? Why are they there?

Where are all the 10s on your multiplication grid? And all the 12s? What can you say about the patterns they make?

Which numbers *don't* appear on your multiplication grid? Why is that?
Which numbers appear most often? Why is that?

Stick a blank 10 x 10 grid onto paper. Make an addition grid for the numbers 1 to 10, using the space outside the square as you need to.
Now make a subtraction grid.
Use these to test your friends on their number bonds.

Rectangles

Imagine any rectangle placed against the top left-hand corner — but don't draw it.
How many squares has the rectangle? Write the number in the bottom right-hand corner of the rectangle.
Go on imagining rectangles and writing the numbers, until every square is filled. What have you produced?

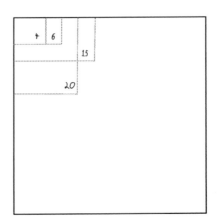

Blank 10 x 10 grid

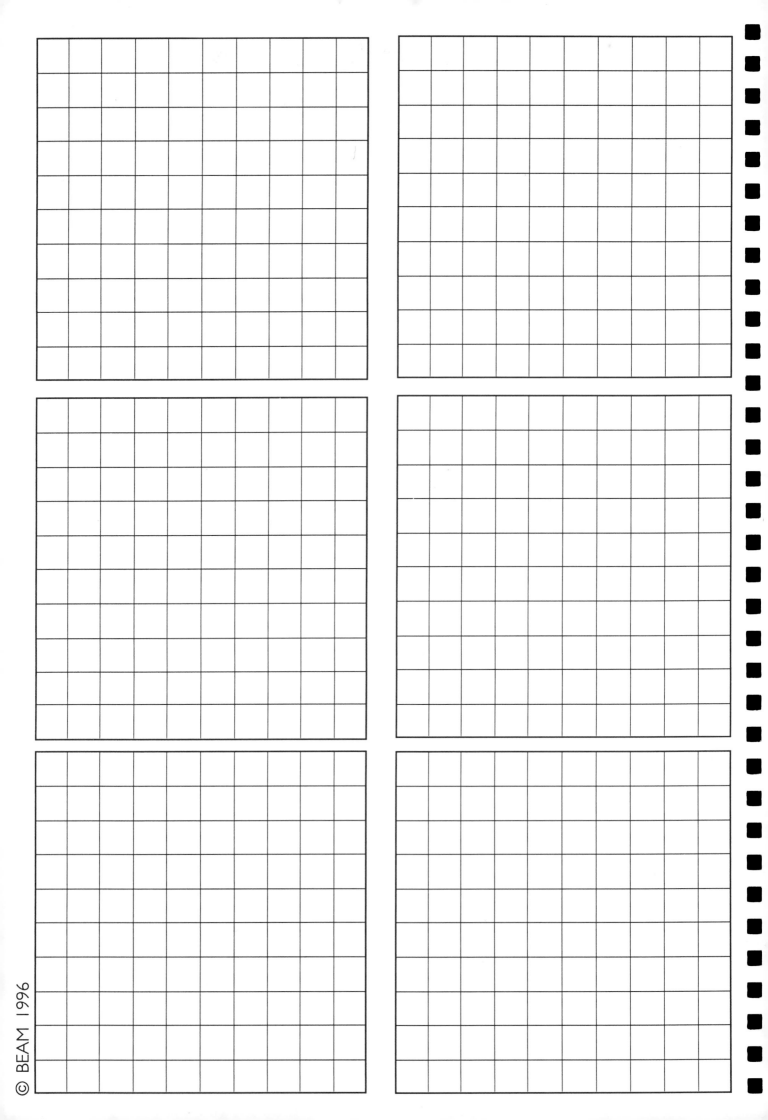

2 x 2, 3 x 3 and 4 x 4 grids

Possibilities

You need lots of 2 x 2 blank grids. What are all the different ways of writing the numbers 1–4 in these squares?

You need lots of 2 x 2 blank grids and four coloured pens. Colour each square a different colour. What are all the different ways of colouring the squares in the grids using those same four colours? (Each square must be just one colour.)

You need lots of 3 x 3 blank grids. Can you find 10 different ways of writing the numbers 1–9 in these squares? 20 different ways?

Patterns

You need a 3 x 3 and 4 x 4 numbered grid (starting at 1). Colour in 2 and 4 and 6 . . . and so on. What patterns do you see?
How do the patterns compare with the pattern of 2s on a 5 x 5 or 10 x 10 numbered grid?

Explorations

You need a 3 x 3 blank grid. Can you write all the numbers from 1 to 9 in order?
Make another 3 x 3 grid where the numbers start in a different place and follow a different pattern. Are any numbers in the same place on two different squares?

You need a 4 x 4 blank grid. Write the numbers 1 to 16 at random in the squares. Now cut out an L-shape to cover three squares. Can you lay the L-shape on the grid so as to cover three numbers that add up to 10?
What is the highest total you can make that way? And the lowest?

2 x 2 grids

3 x 3 grids

1	2	3
4	5	6
7	8	9

1	2	3
4	5	6
7	8	9

1	2	3
4	5	6
7	8	9

1	2	3
4	5	6
7	8	9

1	2	3
4	5	6
7	8	9

1	2	3
4	5	6
7	8	9

4 x 4 grids

<table>
<tr><td></td><td></td><td></td><td></td></tr>
<tr><td></td><td></td><td></td><td></td></tr>
<tr><td></td><td></td><td></td><td></td></tr>
<tr><td></td><td></td><td></td><td></td></tr>
</table>

<table>
<tr><td>1</td><td>2</td><td>3</td><td>4</td></tr>
<tr><td>5</td><td>6</td><td>7</td><td>8</td></tr>
<tr><td>9</td><td>10</td><td>11</td><td>12</td></tr>
<tr><td>13</td><td>14</td><td>15</td><td>16</td></tr>
</table>

<table>
<tr><td></td><td></td><td></td><td></td></tr>
<tr><td></td><td></td><td></td><td></td></tr>
<tr><td></td><td></td><td></td><td></td></tr>
<tr><td></td><td></td><td></td><td></td></tr>
</table>

<table>
<tr><td>1</td><td>2</td><td>3</td><td>4</td></tr>
<tr><td>5</td><td>6</td><td>7</td><td>8</td></tr>
<tr><td>9</td><td>10</td><td>11</td><td>12</td></tr>
<tr><td>13</td><td>14</td><td>15</td><td>16</td></tr>
</table>

<table>
<tr><td></td><td></td><td></td><td></td></tr>
<tr><td></td><td></td><td></td><td></td></tr>
<tr><td></td><td></td><td></td><td></td></tr>
<tr><td></td><td></td><td></td><td></td></tr>
</table>

<table>
<tr><td>1</td><td>2</td><td>3</td><td>4</td></tr>
<tr><td>5</td><td>6</td><td>7</td><td>8</td></tr>
<tr><td>9</td><td>10</td><td>11</td><td>12</td></tr>
<tr><td>13</td><td>14</td><td>15</td><td>16</td></tr>
</table>

5 x 5 grids

Number sequences

You need a blank 5 x 5 grid. Can you write all the numbers from 1 to 25 in order?
Place a cube on any number on your grid. Can your friend tell you what number is hidden?
Can they write that number down?

Place a Centicube on *every* number on your grid. Can you uncover any number your friend asks for?
Leave the cube off if you get it right.

Try the same things with a 5 x 5 grid with all the numbers from 0 to 24 in order.

Make a window frame from Multilink cubes and use it to frame any number — the frame should hide eight other numbers. (Or you could make a frame from card.)
What are the hidden numbers?
Record your work.
Try the same thing with other number grids. Or make a frame that shows two numbers. Or make another shape to cover up some numbers (for instance, make a snake from Multilink).

1				5
6		8		10
11				15
16	17	18	19	20
21	22	23	24	25

Make several 5 x 5 grids where the numbers from 1 to 25 go left to right, up and down, in a spiral . . .
Are any numbers in the same place on two different squares?

Make a 1–25 or 0–24 square grid where the numbers are arranged in a spiral. Cut it up into five pieces, each with five squares on it.
Can your friend fit the pieces back together again?
(Don't tell her it's a spiral.)

Patterns

You need a 5 x 5 grid with the numbers 1 to 25 in order. Colour in 2 and multiples of 2.
How does the pattern compare with the pattern of 2s on a 1–100 square grid?

What pattern do the odd numbers make on your grid? How does the pattern compare to that on a 6 x 6 grid?

Make a variety of 1–25 square grids, where the numbers go left to right, up and down, and so on. Colour in the numbers in the two times table. What patterns do you notice? Are any the same?

21	22	23	24	25
20	7	8	9	10
19	6	1	2	11
18	5	4	3	12
17	16	15	14	13

You need a 1–25 square grid with the numbers in order. Colour in every third/fifth/ninth/tenth square on your grid. What patterns do you notice?
How do the patterns compare with the same pattern on a 1–100 square grid?

What other patterns can you see in the numbers on your grid?

Games

Bingo — a game for 3 or 4 children
Each child needs a 1–25 square grid. They each choose ten numbers to colour in.
They take turns to pick a card from a pack of well-shuffled cards 1 to 25, and read out the number.
Anyone on whose board that number is *not* coloured in covers it with a cube.
The game continues until everybody's numbers are all coloured or covered.

You need a 5 x 5 blank grid. Fill the squares in at random with the numbers from 1 to 25.
Toss two dice and choose whether to add, subtract, divide or multiply those two numbers. Find the answer on the number grid and colour it in.
Aim to colour five squares in a row — across, up and down, or diagonally.
Now play on a grid where the numbers 1 to 25 are in order. What is the difference?
What about using a 0–24 grid?
Now play the game using two dice and just adding the numbers. Make a note of which numbers come up most and make a different grid using this knowledge.
Try the same with just multiplication or just subtraction.

5 x 5 grids

1	2	3	4	5
6	7	8	9	10
11	12	13	14	15
16	17	18	19	20
21	22	23	24	25

1	2	3	4	5
6	7	8	9	10
11	12	13	14	15
16	17	18	19	20
21	22	23	24	25

1	2	3	4	5
6	7	8	9	10
11	12	13	14	15
16	17	18	19	20
21	22	23	24	25

1	2	3	4	5
6	7	8	9	10
11	12	13	14	15
16	17	18	19	20
21	22	23	24	25

5 x 5 grids

0	1	2	3	4
5	6	7	8	9
10	11	12	13	14
15	16	17	18	19
20	21	22	23	24

0	1	2	3	4
5	6	7	8	9
10	11	12	13	14
15	16	17	18	19
20	21	22	23	24

0	1	2	3	4
5	6	7	8	9
10	11	12	13	14
15	16	17	18	19
20	21	22	23	24

0	1	2	3	4
5	6	7	8	9
10	11	12	13	14
15	16	17	18	19
20	21	22	23	24

6 x 6, 7 x 7, 8 x 8 and 9 x 9 grids

Nearly all the activities suggested for the 10 x 10 grid can also be done on these other grids. The aim is to encourage children to look at what is the same and what is different each time, and to try to find explanations for these.

Here we suggest *a few* other activities you might consider using.

Number sequences

Make a 1–36 (or 0–35 or 1–49 . . .) square grid. Make another one using the same numbers where the numbers follow some other pattern. Are any numbers in the same place on two different squares?

Use any number grid. Make an L-shape from card and use it to hide any three numbers on your grid.
Can your friend tell you what the hidden numbers are?
Do the same thing with another shape.

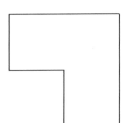

Make a number grid where the numbers are arranged in a spiral. Cut it into several pieces.
Can your friend fit the pieces back together again? (Don't tell her it's a spiral.)
Place a cube on any number on your spiral. Can your friend tell you what number is hidden?
Can they write that number down?

Make a 1–36 square grid on squared paper. What other grids can you make with the numbers 1 to 36? A rectangle? A different rectangle?
Try doing the same thing with numbers 1 to 25, 1 to 49, 1 to 64 or 1 to 81.

Patterns

Choose any square grids. On them, colour in 2 and then all the other multiples of 2. What patterns do you notice?
How do the patterns compare with the pattern of 2s on a 1–100 square grid?

Choose any grid. Try colouring in multiples of each number from 2 to 9 in turn. What patterns do you notice?
How do the patterns compare with the same patterns on a 1–100 square?

Game

Two of you, make a 6 x 6 multiplication grid to share. Take turns to toss two dice (numbered 1 to 6) and multiply the two numbers. Then put a counter on that number on the square. Your aim is to finish a line of four. (You can either aim to complete your own line of four, like in noughts and crosses, or aim to be the person who completes any row.)

x	1	2	3	4	5	6
1	1	●	3	4	5	6
2	2	4	6	●	10	12
3	3	5	9	12	15	18
4	4	●	12	16	20	24
5	5	10	15	20	25	30
6	6	12	18	24	30	36

Could you do the same thing with a 5 x 5 multiplication grid? With an 8 x 8 grid and eight-sided dice?

6 x 6 grids

6 x 6 grids

1	2	3	4	5	6
7	8	9	10	11	12
13	14	15	16	17	18
19	20	21	22	23	24
25	26	27	28	29	30
31	32	33	34	35	36

1	2	3	4	5	6
7	8	9	10	11	12
13	14	15	16	17	18
19	20	21	22	23	24
25	26	27	28	29	30
31	32	33	34	35	36

1	2	3	4	5	6
7	8	9	10	11	12
13	14	15	16	17	18
19	20	21	22	23	24
25	26	27	28	29	30
31	32	33	34	35	36

1	2	3	4	5	6
7	8	9	10	11	12
13	14	15	16	17	18
19	20	21	22	23	24
25	26	27	28	29	30
31	32	33	34	35	36

6 x 6 grids

0	1	2	3	4	5
6	7	8	9	10	11
12	13	14	15	16	17
18	19	20	21	22	23
24	25	26	27	28	29
30	31	32	33	34	35

0	1	2	3	4	5
6	7	8	9	10	11
12	13	14	15	16	17
18	19	20	21	22	23
24	25	26	27	28	29
30	31	32	33	34	35

0	1	2	3	4	5
6	7	8	9	10	11
12	13	14	15	16	17
18	19	20	21	22	23
24	25	26	27	28	29
30	31	32	33	34	35

0	1	2	3	4	5
6	7	8	9	10	11
12	13	14	15	16	17
18	19	20	21	22	23
24	25	26	27	28	29
30	31	32	33	34	35

7 x 7 grids

7 x 7 grids

1	2	3	4	5	6	7
8	9	10	11	12	13	14
15	16	17	18	19	20	21
22	23	24	25	26	27	28
29	30	31	32	33	34	35
36	37	38	39	40	41	42
43	44	45	46	47	48	49

1	2	3	4	5	6	7
8	9	10	11	12	13	14
15	16	17	18	19	20	21
22	23	24	25	26	27	28
29	30	31	32	33	34	35
36	37	38	39	40	41	42
43	44	45	46	47	48	49

0	1	2	3	4	5	6
7	8	9	10	11	12	13
14	15	16	17	18	19	20
21	22	23	24	25	26	27
28	29	30	31	32	33	34
35	36	37	38	39	40	41
42	43	44	45	46	47	48

8 x 8 grids

8 x 8 grids

1	2	3	4	5	6	7	8
9	10	11	12	13	14	15	16
17	18	19	20	21	22	23	24
25	26	27	28	29	30	31	32
33	34	35	36	37	38	39	40
41	42	43	44	45	46	47	48
49	50	51	52	53	54	55	56
57	58	59	60	61	62	63	64

1	2	3	4	5	6	7	8
9	10	11	12	13	14	15	16
17	18	19	20	21	22	23	24
25	26	27	28	29	30	31	32
33	34	35	36	37	38	39	40
41	42	43	44	45	46	47	48
49	50	51	52	53	54	55	56
57	58	59	60	61	62	63	64

0	1	2	3	4	5	6	7
8	9	10	11	12	13	14	15
16	17	18	19	20	21	22	23
24	25	26	27	28	29	30	31
32	33	34	35	36	37	38	39
40	41	42	43	44	45	46	47
48	49	50	51	52	53	54	55
56	57	58	59	60	61	62	63

9 x 9 grids

9 x 9 grids

1	2	3	4	5	6	7	8	9
10	11	12	13	14	15	16	17	18
19	20	21	22	23	24	25	26	27
28	29	30	31	32	33	34	35	36
37	38	39	40	41	42	43	44	45
46	47	48	49	50	51	52	53	54
55	56	57	58	59	60	61	62	63
64	65	66	67	68	69	70	71	72
73	74	75	76	77	78	79	80	81

0	1	2	3	4	5	6	7	8
9	10	11	12	13	14	15	16	17
18	19	20	21	22	23	24	25	26
27	28	29	30	31	32	33	34	35
36	37	38	39	40	41	42	43	44
45	46	47	48	49	50	51	52	53
54	55	56	57	58	59	60	61	62
63	64	65	66	67	68	69	70	71
72	73	74	75	76	77	78	79	80

1	2	3	4	5	6	7	8	9
10	11	12	13	14	15	16	17	18
19	20	21	22	23	24	25	26	27
28	29	30	31	32	33	34	35	36
37	38	39	40	41	42	43	44	45
46	47	48	49	50	51	52	53	54
55	56	57	58	59	60	61	62	63
64	65	66	67	68	69	70	71	72
73	74	75	76	77	78	79	80	81

0	1	2	3	4	5	6	7	8
9	10	11	12	13	14	15	16	17
18	19	20	21	22	23	24	25	26
27	28	29	30	31	32	33	34	35
36	37	38	39	40	41	42	43	44
45	46	47	48	49	50	51	52	53
54	55	56	57	58	59	60	61	62
63	64	65	66	67	68	69	70	71
72	73	74	75	76	77	78	79	80

9 x 9 grid

1	2	3	4	5	6	7	8	9
10	11	12	13	14	15	16	17	18
19	20	21	22	23	24	25	26	27
28	29	30	31	32	33	34	35	36
37	38	39	40	41	42	43	44	45
46	47	48	49	50	51	52	53	54
55	56	57	58	59	60	61	62	63
64	65	66	67	68	69	70	71	72
73	74	75	76	77	78	79	80	81

Oblong number grids

Nearly all the activities suggested for the 10 x 10 grid can also be done on oblong grids. However, the significance of using oblong grids is to show that the choice of a square of numbers is quite arbitrary, and the important thing is how many numbers there are in each row. That decided one can obviously have as many rows as one likes.

It is useful when dealing with the square grids to ask occasionally what will happen with larger numbers. Using the oblong grids will enable children to explore in more detail some particular ideas and test some earlier hypotheses. For example:

— *square numbers*, on a 10-in-a-row grid, continue to have the same sequence of last digits

— *prime numbers*, on a 6-in-a-row grid, continue to appear in the same two columns

— *prime numbers*, on a 10-in-a-row grid, continue to appear irregularly, with different numbers of them in each row; however, the 10 x 200 grid will make it easier to explore primes between 100 and 200.

Oblong number grids

1	2	3	4	5
6	7	8	9	10
11	12	13	14	15
16	17	18	19	20
21	22	23	24	25
26	27	28	29	30
31	32	33	34	35
36	37	38	39	40
41	42	43	44	45
46	47	48	49	50
51	52	53	54	55
56	57	58	59	60
61	62	63	64	65
66	67	68	69	70
71	72	73	74	75
76	77	78	79	80
81	82	83	84	85
86	87	88	89	90
91	92	93	94	95
96	97	98	99	100

1	2	3	4	5	6
7	8	9	10	11	12
13	14	15	16	17	18
19	20	21	22	23	24
25	26	27	28	29	30
31	32	33	34	35	36
37	38	39	40	41	42
43	44	45	46	47	48
49	50	51	52	53	54
55	56	57	58	59	60
61	62	63	64	65	66
67	68	69	70	71	72
73	74	75	76	77	78
79	80	81	82	83	84
85	86	87	88	89	90
91	92	93	94	95	96
97	98	99	100	101	102

1	2	3	4	5	6	7	8	9	10
11	12	13	14	15	16	17	18	19	20
21	22	23	24	25	26	27	28	29	30
31	32	33	34	35	36	37	38	39	40
41	42	43	44	45	46	47	48	49	50
51	52	53	54	55	56	57	58	59	60
61	62	63	64	65	66	67	68	69	70
71	72	73	74	75	76	77	78	79	80
81	82	83	84	85	86	87	88	89	90
91	92	93	94	95	96	97	98	99	100
101	102	103	104	105	106	107	108	109	110
111	112	113	114	115	116	117	118	119	120
121	122	123	124	125	126	127	128	129	130
131	132	133	134	135	136	137	138	139	140
141	142	143	144	145	146	147	148	149	150
151	152	153	154	155	156	157	158	159	160
161	162	163	164	165	166	167	168	169	170
171	172	173	174	175	176	177	178	179	180
181	182	183	184	185	186	187	188	189	190
191	192	193	194	195	196	197	198	199	200

0-99 grids

Making numbers

You need two 0 to 9 spinners. Put cubes on any ten numbers on the 0–99 square, then spin the spinners. Can you use those two numbers to make any of the numbers you covered? If you can, remove that number.

Go on until you have removed all the cubes. (At a simple level numbers can be 'made' by combining the two digits. For example, a 3 and 4 could make 34 or 43. At a more advanced level children can add, subtract or multiply those two numbers.)

Spin two 0 to 9 spinners to make as many different one-digit or two-digit numbers as you can. As you make each one, cover it on the 0–99 square. Can you eventually get all the numbers?

You need two sets of cards 0 to 9. Mark 'tens' on each card of one set and 'units' on each card of the other. Shuffle each set and put it face down on the table.

Pick the top card from each set and put the two together to make a number. Cover that number on the 0–99 square.

Go on like that until the cards run out. What are all the numbers you have coloured?

Hidden numbers

Make a wide picture frame with card and use it to frame any number.
What are the numbers hidden behind the frame?
Record your work.
Try making a frame that shows two numbers.

Multiple patterns

Look at the first column. What numbers does it contain?
Are you happy that 0 is there? Should it be, and why?
Is 0 a multiple of 10? If so, how many tens is it?

Look at the diagonal going from top left to bottom right. What numbers does it contain? Are you happy that it includes 0? Should it?
Is 0 a multiple of 11? If so, how many elevens is it?

Shade in 3, and then every other multiple of 3. What pattern do you notice? What should you do about the 0? Why do you think that?
How does the pattern compare to the pattern of threes on a 1–100 square?

Is 0 included in the other sets of multiples? Explain your ideas about this.

Is 0 a prime number? Explain your ideas about this.

Shade in all the even numbers with strokes, like this. What pattern do you notice?
Now colour all the multiples of 3 with strokes going the other way.
Which numbers are shaded twice? Why is that?
Which numbers have no shading on them? What does that mean?
How does the pattern compare to the similar pattern on a 1–100 square?

What would you expect to happen if you did the same thing with the multiples of 4 and multiples of 6? Try it. Were you right?

What will happen with multiples of 3 and multiples of 6? And other pairs of multiples?

What about *three* sets of multiples — say, those of 3, 4 and 5?

Overlays

Imagine the 0–99 grid put on top of the 1–100 grid. If necessary, make a tracing (or photocopy it onto transparent film) and actually put it on. Add each number to the one below it. What do you get? Why is that?

Make a tracing of the 0–99 grid (or photocopy it onto transparent film), put it on top of another 0–99 grid, and slide it along one square. Add each pair of corresponding numbers. What do you get? Why is that?
What happens if you slide the grid two squares along? One place down? Two places down?
Turn your overlay upside down and put it on top of the 0–99 grid again. Add each number to the one below it and notice what happens. ('Upside down' can mean several different things — try them all.)

Give your overlay a quarter turn and add numbers as before. What happens?
Now try a quarter turn the other way.

Games

You need two sets of cards 0 to 9. Shuffle them together and put them face down on the table. Take turns to pick three cards and use them to make any number on the square — you can add, subtract, multiply, divide, and put numbers together any way you like.
For instance, with 2, 5 and 4 you could do 25 + 4 = 29.
Colour in your number on the square.
The first person to get five numbers in a row (horizontally, vertically or diagonally) is the winner.

Invent a game for two people to play on a 0–99 square that involves dice and counters.
Write the rules down so other people can play it too. You could illustrate your explanation with pictures or diagrams.

Devise a number quiz where the answers form a pattern on a 0–99 square. Do the quiz with your group. Does everyone get the pattern?

0–99 grid

0	1	2	3	4	5	6	7	8	9
10	11	12	13	14	15	16	17	18	19
20	21	22	23	24	25	26	27	28	29
30	31	32	33	34	35	36	37	38	39
40	41	42	43	44	45	46	47	48	49
50	51	52	53	54	55	56	57	58	59
60	61	62	63	64	65	66	67	68	69
70	71	72	73	74	75	76	77	78	79
80	81	82	83	84	85	86	87	88	89
90	91	92	93	94	95	96	97	98	99

1-100 spirals

Making number spirals

Use a blank 1–100 grid, start in one of the centre places and write the numbers from 1 to 100 in a spiral.

Compare your spiral with those of your friends. How many different spirals have you made? How many different spirals are there?

What numbers are next to each other on your spiral? Is there any pattern?

Compare your spiral with those of your friends. Are any numbers in the same place on different spirals?

Jigsaw

Cut the spiral into five pieces (or three, or six . . .).
Can you fit the pieces back together again?
Can your friend fit the pieces back together again?

Hidden numbers

Place a cube on any number on the spiral. Can your friend tell you what number is hidden?
Can they write that number down?

Patterns

Can you see what pattern would be made by the even numbers, without colouring them in?
Can you see where the square numbers are? Explain this.
Where are the odd square numbers and the even square numbers? Explain this.

Colour in the multiples of 3. Can you see how they continue? Make a larger spiral to check.
Colour in other sets of multiples to see what patterns they make. Try to see how they continue.

Colour in the prime numbers.

Square rings

The first four numbers are in a square.

$$1 \quad 2$$
$$4 \quad 3$$

How many numbers are in the square surrounding those numbers?

7	8	9	10
6			11
5			12
16	15	14	13

How many numbers are in the next surrounding ring? And so on.

Sequences

Start from 2 and look along the numbers to the right:

2, 11, 28, 53, 86.

What number would come next in the sequence? It may help to look at the differences between the numbers:

$$2 \quad 11 \quad 28 \quad 53 \quad 86$$
$$9 \quad 17 \quad 25 \quad 33$$

How do the differences increase?
Continue the sequence until you get a multiple of 3. Can you explain what happens?
Find other lines of numbers starting from the centre that do not contain a multiple of 3.
Will the above sequence ever contain a multiple of 5?

Start from 1 and move along the numbers downwards. Explore this sequence. Do you ever get a multiple of 7?
Start from another number and move along the row or column outwards. What sort of sequences of numbers do you get? What is the same about them all?

Start from 3 and move along the numbers diagonally down to the right:

3, 13, 31, 57, 91.

What happens now? Will you ever get a multiple of 5?

Explore other diagonal lines.

1-100 spiral

73	74	75	76	77	78	79	80	81	82
72	43	44	45	46	47	48	49	50	83
71	42	21	22	23	24	25	26	51	84
70	41	20	7	8	9	10	27	52	85
69	40	19	6	1	2	11	28	53	86
68	39	18	5	4	3	12	29	54	87
67	38	17	16	15	14	13	30	55	88
66	37	36	35	34	33	32	31	56	89
65	64	63	62	61	60	59	58	57	90
100	99	98	97	96	95	94	93	92	91

Multiplication charts

Hidden numbers

Place a cube on any number on the multiplication grid.
Can your friend tell you what number is hidden?
Can they write that number down?

Learning the tables

Make a multiplication chart from squared paper.

Use the chart provided, or the one you have made, when you need to know multiplication facts.

Use the chart to learn your multiplication tables.
Get a friend to test you on them.

Mark the ones you don't find it easy to remember.
How can you memorise them?

Diagonals

What numbers are in the diagonal going from top left to bottom right? Why?

Look at diagonal lines of numbers (top left to bottom right) starting from 2, or 3, or 4 . . . .. How do they continue? What is the rule for each one? What rule do they all have?

Neighbours

Without looking at the grid, say which numbers can come to the right of 8. What about 12? And 24? And 25, 30, 36?

Without looking at the grid, say which number comes between: 5 and 7; 9 and 15; 24 and 36; 20 and 30; 32 and 48.

Say which *two* numbers come between: 10 and 25; 8 and 20; 21 and 30; 21 and 42.
Make up similar questions for someone else.

Patterns

Colour all the 8s, 10s and 12s on your multiplication grid, using a different colour for each number. What can you say about the patterns each number makes?

Numbers of times

Which numbers appear most times in this grid?
Why is this?
If you could make the grid as big as you liked, where else would 24 occur?
Which numbers occur only once? Why?
Which numbers occur only twice? Why?
Which numbers occur an odd number of times? Why?
Which numbers occur only three times? Why?
Which numbers do not appear at all?

Opposite corners

Choose a square of four numbers anywhere on the grid. Multiply opposite corners together. What happens?
Does the same thing happen with other squares?
Why does this happen?

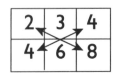

Find the numbers 20, 24, 42 and 35.
Are they at the corners of a square? Does the same thing happen again if you multiply numbers at opposite corners?
Find some other squares like this and try again.

What happens with other rectangles?

What happens with parallelograms? Other shapes?

10 x 10 multiplication chart

x	1	2	3	4	5	6	7	8	9	10
1	1	2	3	4	5	6	7	8	9	10
2	2	4	6	8	10	12	14	16	18	20
3	3	6	9	12	15	18	21	24	27	30
4	4	8	12	16	20	24	28	32	36	40
5	5	10	15	20	25	30	35	40	45	50
6	6	12	18	24	30	36	42	48	54	60
7	7	14	21	28	35	42	49	56	63	70
8	8	16	24	32	40	48	56	64	72	80
9	9	18	27	36	45	54	63	72	81	90
10	10	20	30	40	50	60	70	80	90	100

12 x 12 multiplication chart

1	2	3	4	5	6	7	8	9	10	11	12
2	4	6	8	10	12	14	16	18	20	22	24
3	6	9	12	15	18	21	24	27	30	33	36
4	8	12	16	20	24	28	32	36	40	44	48
5	10	15	20	25	30	35	40	45	50	55	60
6	12	18	24	30	36	42	48	54	60	66	72
7	14	21	28	35	42	49	56	63	70	77	84
8	16	24	32	40	48	56	64	72	80	88	96
9	18	27	36	45	54	63	72	81	90	99	108
10	20	30	40	50	60	70	80	90	100	110	120
11	22	33	44	55	66	77	88	99	110	121	132
12	24	36	48	60	72	84	96	108	120	132	144

1-144 grids

Many of the activities suggested for the 10 x 10 grid can also be done on these grids. The aim is to encourage children to look at what is the same and what is different each time, and to try to find explanations for these.

Here we suggest a few of the activities you might consider using.

Patterns

Explore patterns made by the multiplication tables. In particular, can you predict which tables are not going to give vertical lines? Which tables are going to give diagonal lines? Which are going to give knight's moves?
How do the patterns compare to those on other grids?

Colour in the square numbers. What do you notice? Which columns do they come in? Why is this? How does the pattern compare to those on other grids?
If the 144 square were continued downwards (i.e. past 144), would those columns still be the only ones with squares in?

Explore the triangular numbers in the same way.

Explore the cubes.

Where do the prime numbers come? (Compare this with the 1–36 grid.)

Moves

Start on any number. What number comes below it? Repeat this with other numbers. What happens each time? What would happen with numbers on the bottom row if the chart were continued?
What happens if you move two down each time?

Start on any number. Move one to the right and one down. What number are you on?
Repeat this with other numbers. What happens each time? Can you explain this?

1–144 grid

1	2	3	4	5	6	7	8	9	10	11	12
13	14	15	16	17	18	19	20	21	22	23	24
25	26	27	28	29	30	31	32	33	34	35	36
37	38	39	40	41	42	43	44	45	46	47	48
49	50	51	52	53	54	55	56	57	58	59	60
61	62	63	64	65	66	67	68	69	70	71	72
73	74	75	76	77	78	79	80	81	82	83	84
85	86	87	88	89	90	91	92	93	94	95	96
97	98	99	100	101	102	103	104	105	106	107	108
109	110	111	112	113	114	115	116	117	118	119	120
121	122	123	124	125	126	127	128	129	130	131	132
133	134	135	136	137	138	139	140	141	142	143	144

Large number tiles
0 to 9

Numbers in order

We have a number tile for each number from 0 to 9. How many tiles is that?
We need one person to hold each tile . . . Now, can you put yourselves in order?

Everybody close your eyes. I'm going to touch two people, and they must open their eyes and swap places quietly . . .
Now open your eyes. Who were the people who swapped places?
This time I'm going to get three people to swap places . . .

Number track games

Here are some large tiles numbered 0 to 9. Lay them in order with a space between them, like stepping stones. Now, one of you, go and stand on 0.
The other people, you take turns to toss the dice numbered 0, 0, 1, 1, 2, 2 and tell the person on the line how many steps she is to take . . . What number will she land on?
What number do you need to get to move her on to the 9?

Now we will play a similar game. But this time I'll whisper to the person what number to start on and how many steps to take (forwards or backwards). The rest of you must try and work out what the instructions were.

Here are some tiles numbered 0 to 9. Lay them in order with a space between them, like stepping stones. Now go and stand on 0.
Toss a dice numbered 0, 0, 1, 1, 2, 2 (or 1, 1, 1, 2, 2, 3) and take that many steps forwards (one step per tile). What number have you landed on?
You've got a '0' — what does that mean?
You've got a '1' — where will you land?
You've got a '2' — where will you land this time?
How many steps do you need to take to get to the end?
Now stand on the 9 and toss the dice to take steps back towards 0.

Other ideas

Use large tiles numbered 1 to 9. Lay them out in a line or rectangle and take turns to throw two bean bags onto them.
What numbers have they landed on? Which is the higher/lower number?
Can you add those numbers?
Can you find the difference between those numbers?
Now try throwing three bean bags.

Get into pairs and take a number tile each. Hold the tiles in front of you. Now arrange yourselves in your pair to make a two-digit number. What is it?
Can you make a different two-digit number?
Now get into threes. What is the highest/lowest three-digit number you can make?

Adding

We have a number tile for each number from 0 to 9. Everybody take one tile . . . Now find a person whose number, added to yours, makes 9.
Did anyone get left out? Why not?
I'll deal out the tiles again so everybody has a different number . . . Now find a person whose number, added to yours, makes 10.
Did anyone get left out?
Now find a person whose number, added to yours, makes 9 (or 6 or 12).
Did anyone get left out? Why?

Halving

We have a number tile for each number from 0 to 9. Everybody take one tile . . .
Halve your number in your head and go and find the person with that number. Has everybody got someone to go to?
Double your number in your head and go and find the person with that number. Has everybody got someone to go to?

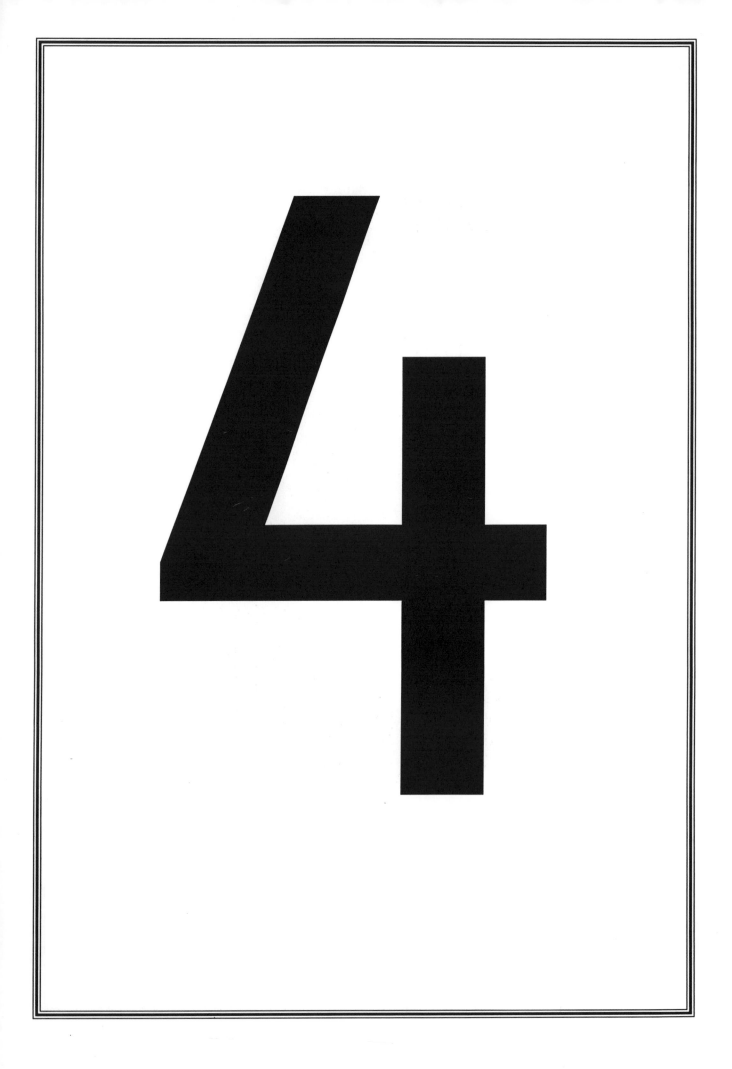

© BEAM 1996

Small number tiles from -10 to 30

Numbers in order

Can you put the tiles 1 to 10 (or 0 to 9, or 0 to 10) in order?
Now turn them all over so they are face down. Can you find number 5? Number 7?

Put the tiles 1 to 10 in order on the table.
I'm going to swap two around while you close your eyes . . . Which two did I swap?
Suppose I swapped three tiles around?

You need a large 1–30 grid (perhaps made from number tiles stuck down onto a board). Can you put the tiles 1 to 30 in place on the grid?

You need a large blank grid with 30 squares. Can you put the tiles 1 to 30 in place on this board?
Close your eyes while I swap two of them around . . .
Now open them. Can you see which two I swapped?

Can you put the tiles from −10 to 10 in order, as they are on the number line?
Turn them all over so they are face down. Can you find number 5 now ? And 0? And −7?

Counting

Lay the tiles from 0 to 10 out in order. Count out the right number of cubes to match the number on each tile, and arrange those cubes in a pattern.
Now close your eyes while I hide one . . .
Open your eyes. Where did I take a cube from?
Now it's your turn to hide a cube.

Put the tiles 0 to 10 in order. Can you put the right number of cubes on each tile, to match the number on the tile? Make them into sticks.
Close your eyes while I swap over two sticks . . .
Now open them. Which two did I swap?
Close your eyes while I add a cube to one stick. . .
Now open them. Where did I add an extra cube?

Adding

We have a number tile for each number from 0 to 20. Everybody take one tile . . . Now find one person whose number, added to yours, makes 20.
Who got left out? What is that number?
I'll deal out the tiles again so everybody has a different number . . . Now, again, find a person whose number, added to yours, makes 20.
Who got left out this time? Why was it the same number?

Now find a person whose number, with yours, adds up to 19 (or 21, 25, 30 . . .).
Who got left out? What is that number?

Halving

We have a number tile for each number from 0 to 20. Everybody take one tile . . .
Halve your number in your head and go and find the person with that number. Has everybody got someone to go to?
Double your number in your head and go and find the person with that number. Has everybody got someone to go to?

Other ideas

Can you arrange the number tiles 1 to 30 as on a number grid?
What other rectangular arrays can you put them in?

1	2	3	4	5	6
7	8	9	10	11	12
13	14	15	16	17	18
19	20	21	22	23	24
25	26	27	28	29	30

What about tiles 1 to 25? Or 1 to 24?

Rows with tiles 0–9

Put all the tiles in order from 0 to 9.
Put all the tiles in order from 9 down to 0.
Put all the tiles in a row so that no tiles next to each other have a difference of 1. (For example, 3 and 4 can't go together, and nor can 7 and 6.)

Put all the tiles in a row so that the numbers alternately increase and decrease.

Put all the tiles in a row so that all the differences between them, except one, are 2.

Put all the tiles in a row so that the differences between them are either 2 or 3.

Put all the tiles in a row so that the differences are alternately 2 and 5.

Put all the tiles in a row so that the differences are alternately 1 and 2.

Put eight of the tiles in a row so that the differences are alternately 2 and 3.

Can you put all the tiles in a row so that the differences are either 2 or 4?

Rows with tiles 1–30

Put the tiles in order from 1 to 30.
Put the tiles in a row so that no tiles next to each other have any digits in common.
Put the tiles in a row so that all tiles next to each other have at least one digit in common.

Zigzags with tiles 1–9

Put the tiles in a zigzag like an upside down L.
The zig and the zag must have the same totals.
See how many different numbers you can choose for the corner tile.

Put the tiles in this zigzag so that each zig and each zag totals 14.
Rearrange them so that each total is 16.
Rearrange them so that the totals are consecutively 13, 14, 15 and 16.

Put the tiles in this zigzag so that successive zigs and zags are consecutive numbers.

Triangles with tiles 1–9

Put the tiles in this triangle so that the total of the numbers along each side is 20.
What other totals can you choose for each side so that they are all the same?

Can you make the totals of the sides 11, 12 and 13?
What other possible totals are consecutive numbers?

Squares with tiles 1–9

Put the tiles in this square so that each row and each column has the same total.

Can you make the two diagonals have the same total as well?
This is known as a Magic Square.
Can you make larger magic squares using the numbers 1 to 16, or 1 to 25?

Put the tiles 1–9 in the square so that each row and each column has a different total.
Can you make the two diagonals have different totals

Squares with tiles 1–8

Put the tiles in this square so that the total of the numbers along each side is 12.
How many different ways can this be done?
Can you make each side total something else?

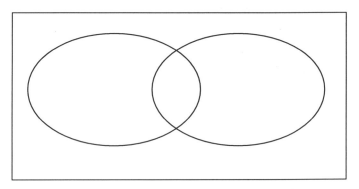

Put the tiles in the square so that the totals of the sides are all different.

Put the tiles in the square so that the totals of the sides are all different, but odd.

Put the tiles in the square so that the totals of the sides are all different, but even.

Totals

In each of the following, arrange the tiles so that each row or column or side has the same total.

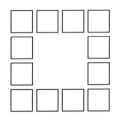

tiles 1 to 12

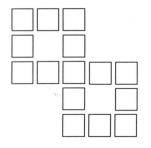

tiles 1 to 15
(hint: their total is 27)

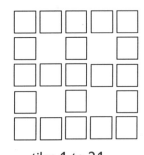

tiles 1 to 21
(hint: their total is 46)

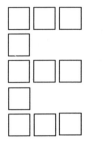

tiles 1 to 11

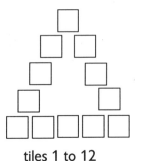

tiles 1 to 12

Sorting into two sets

Sort the tiles into odd numbers and even numbers.

Use a two-set Venn diagram and put the tiles in the right places if the two sets are:
multiples of 3, multiples of 4;
multiples of 4, multiples of 6;
multiples of 3, multiples of 6.
What do you notice?
What other pairs of sets would give the same sort of results as each of these?

Do the same thing for:
square numbers, triangular numbers;
square numbers, cubes;
odd numbers, prime numbers;
even numbers, square numbers;
numbers ending in 7, prime numbers;
numbers ending in 7, square numbers.
Make up some other examples.

Sorting into three sets

Use a three-set Venn diagram and put the tiles in the right places if the three sets are:
multiples of 3, multiples of 4, multiples of 5;
multiples of 4, multiples of 5, multiples of 6;
multiples of 3, multiples of 6, multiples of 9.
Make up your own examples.

1	2	3
4	5	6
7	8	9
10	11	12

13	14	15
16	17	18
19	20	21
22	23	24

25	26	27
28	29	30
-1	-2	-3
-4	-5	-6

-7 -8 -9

-10